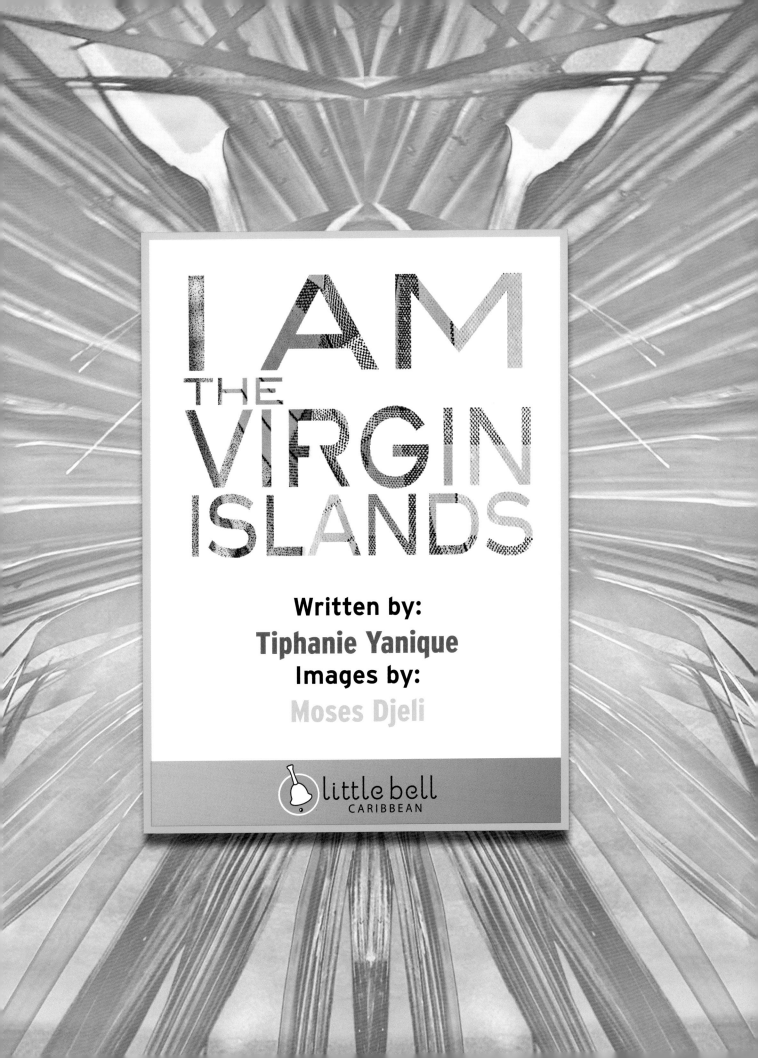

I AM THE VIRGIN ISLANDS

Written by:

Tiphanie Yanique

Images by:

Moses Djeli

little bell
CARIBBEAN

I AM

Coki Beach
and
Cruz Bay
sunrise.

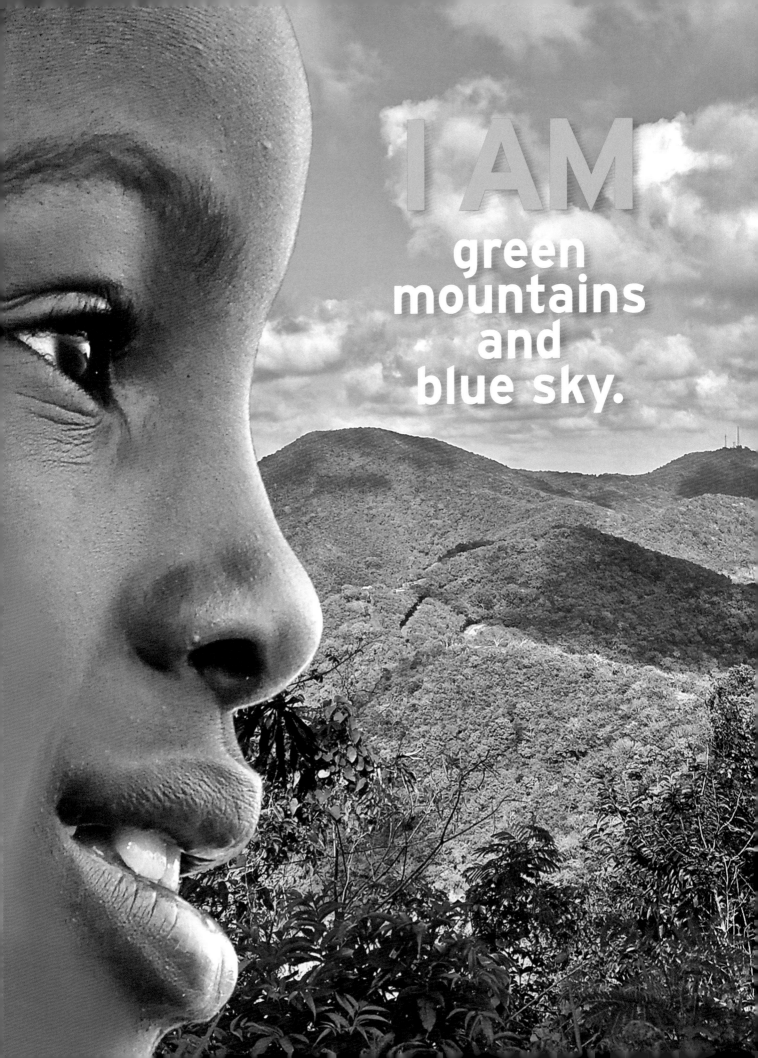

I AM

green
mountains
and
blue sky.

I AM
scratch band
and steel pan.

I AM
Carnival
and Christmas.

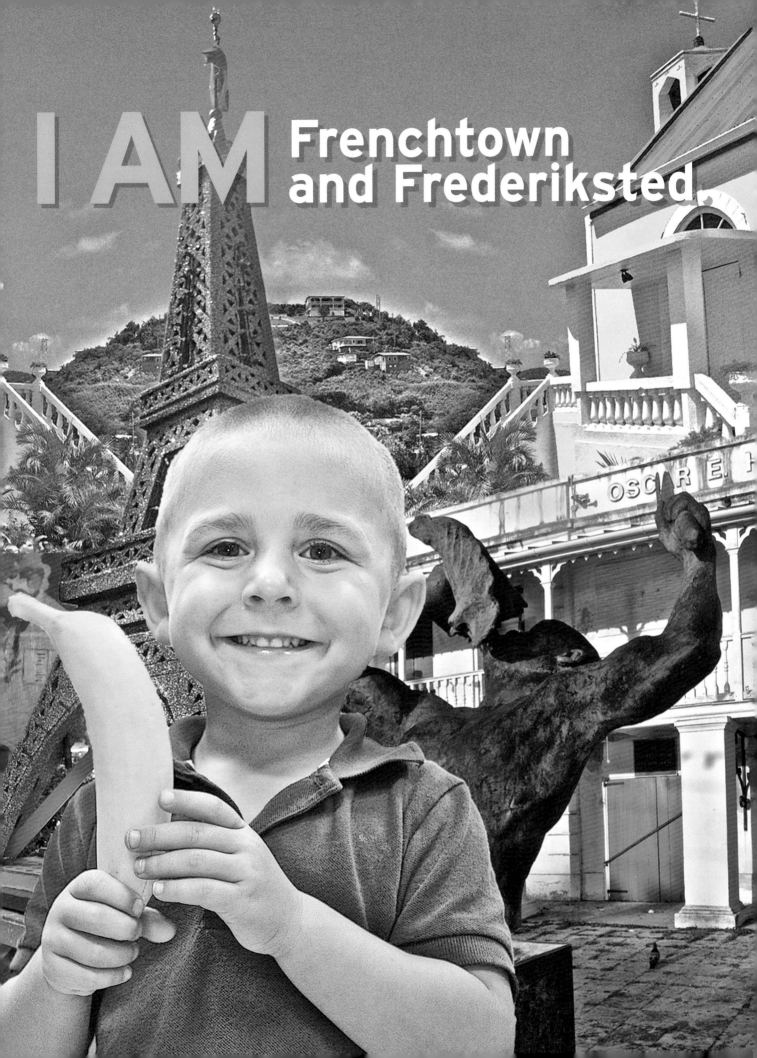

I AM **Frenchtown and Frederiksted.**

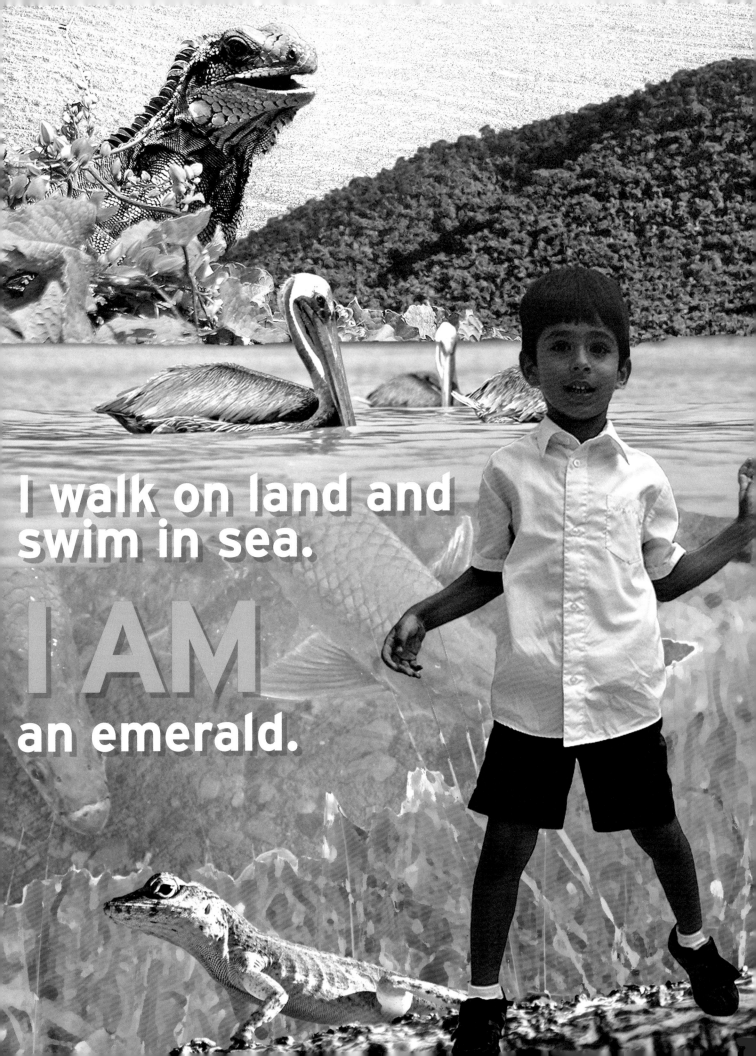

I walk on land and swim in sea.

I AM

an emerald.

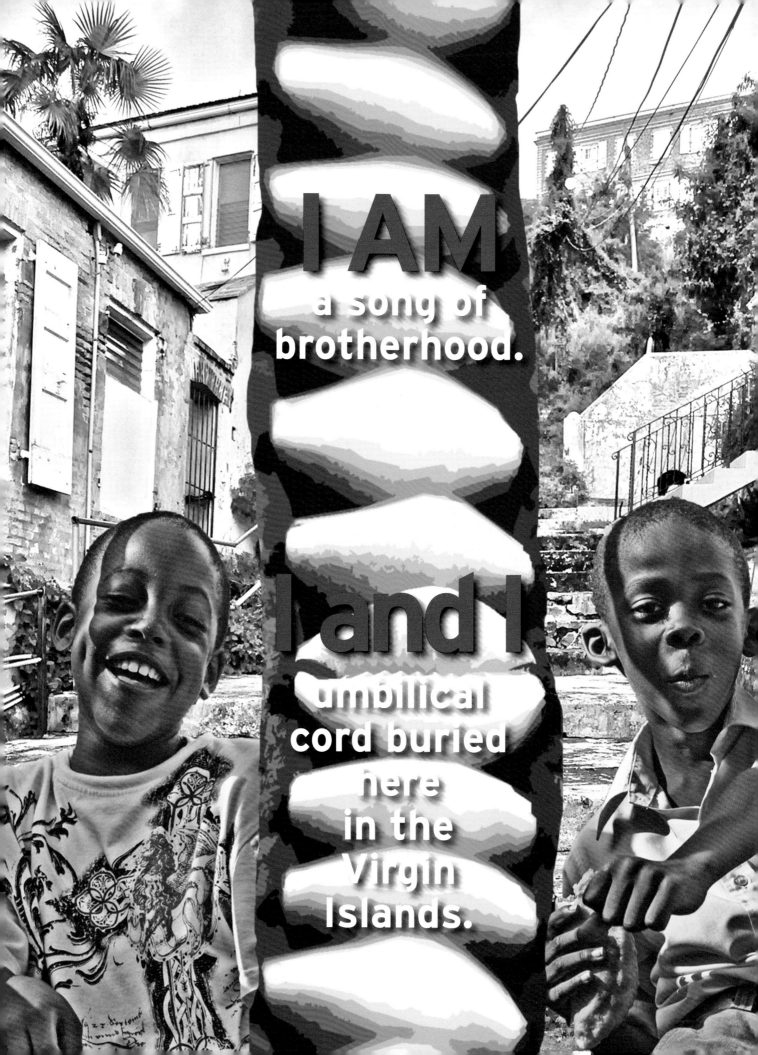

I AM a song of brotherhood.

I and I umbilical cord buried here in the Virgin Islands.

Call me Queen Mary or Coziah; I beat my silent drum.

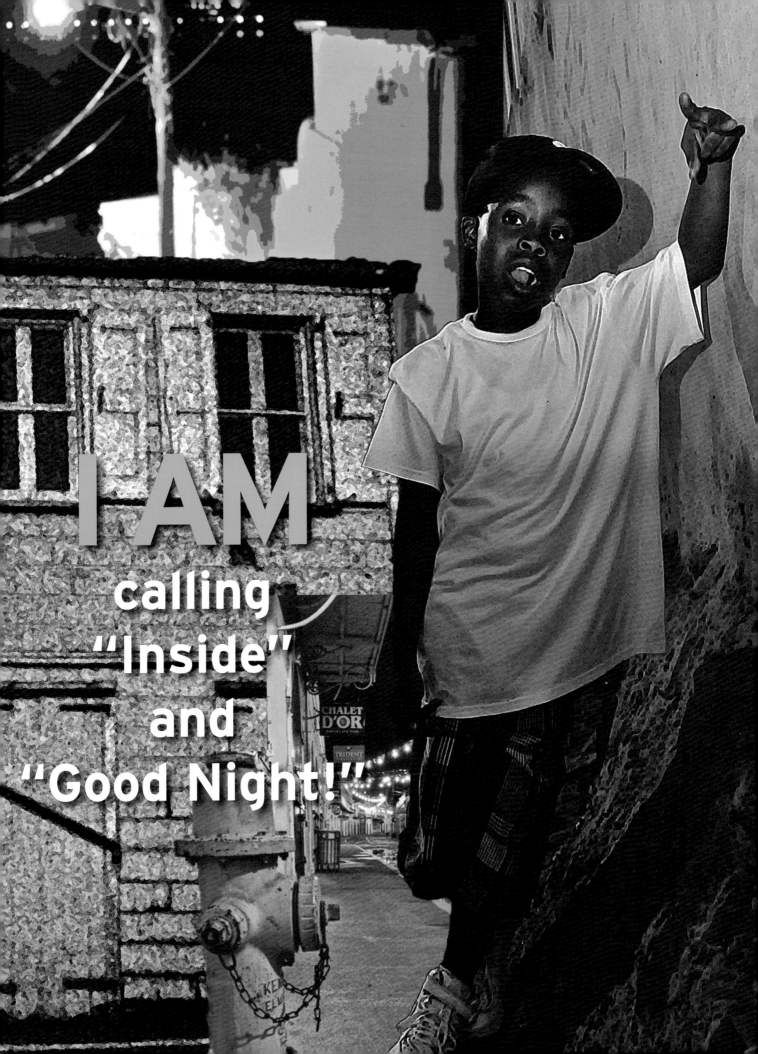

I AM

calling
"Inside"
and
"Good Night!"

I am calling to my
Virgin Islands.

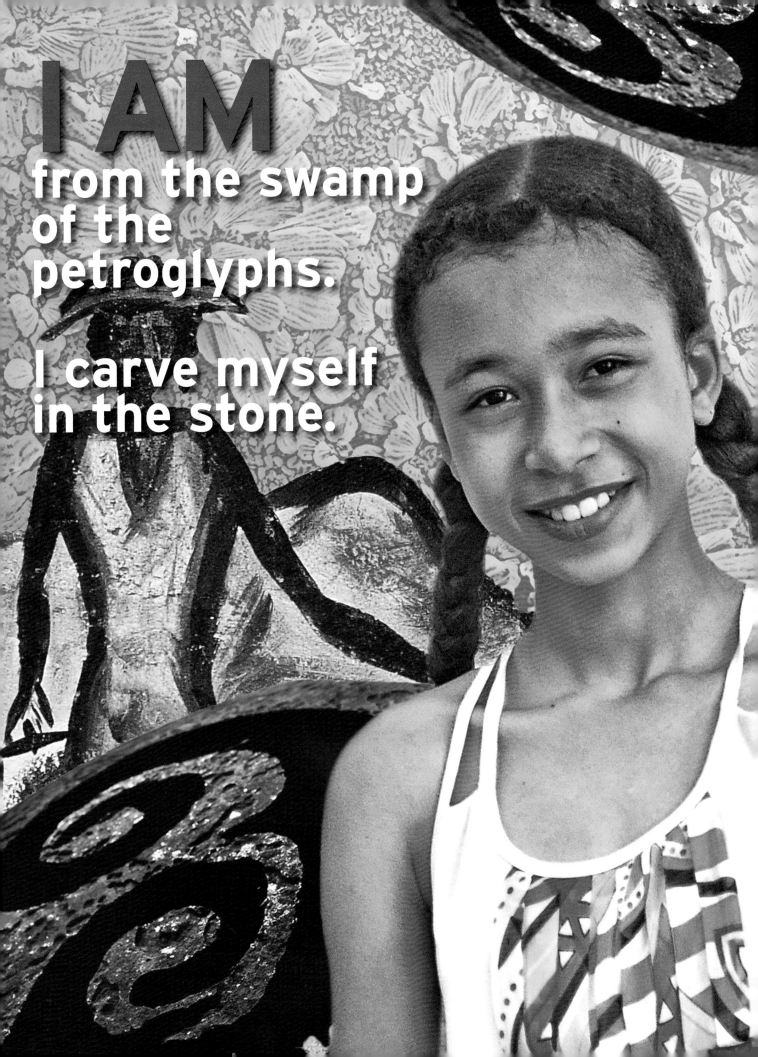

I AM from the swamp of the petroglyphs.

I carve myself in the stone.

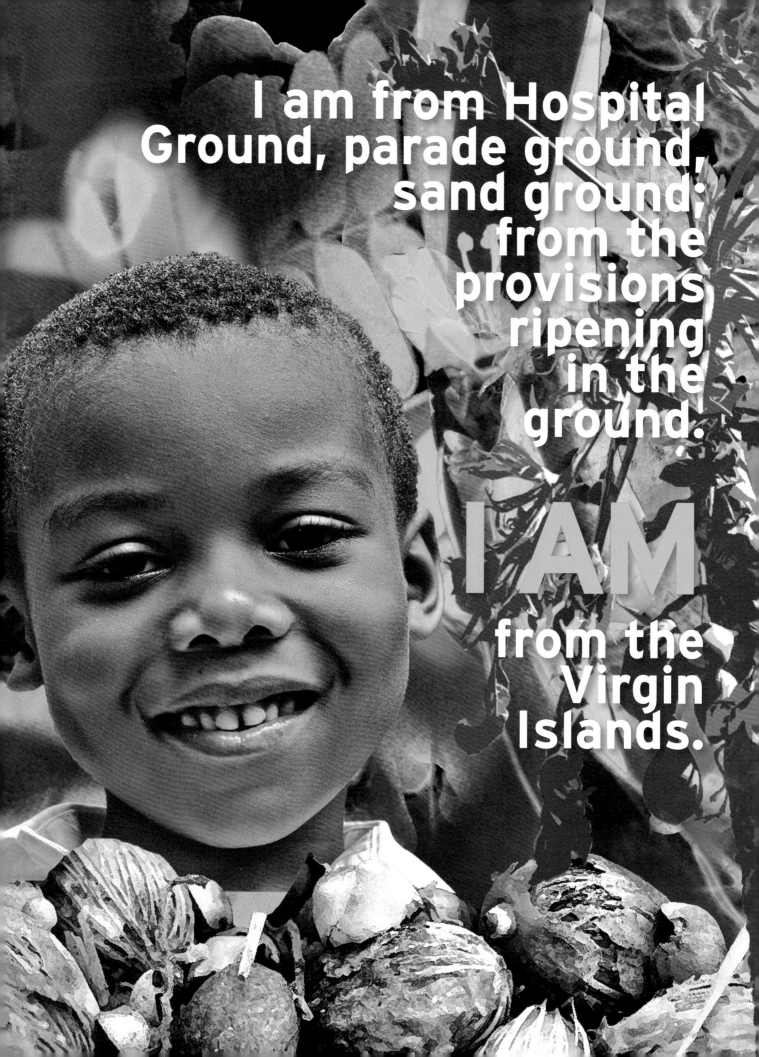

I am from Hospital Ground, parade ground, sand ground; from the provisions ripening in the ground.

I AM

from the Virgin Islands.

I believe
in dominoes
banging
wood tables.

I believe
in madras cloth
stitched
with a white
frilled hem.

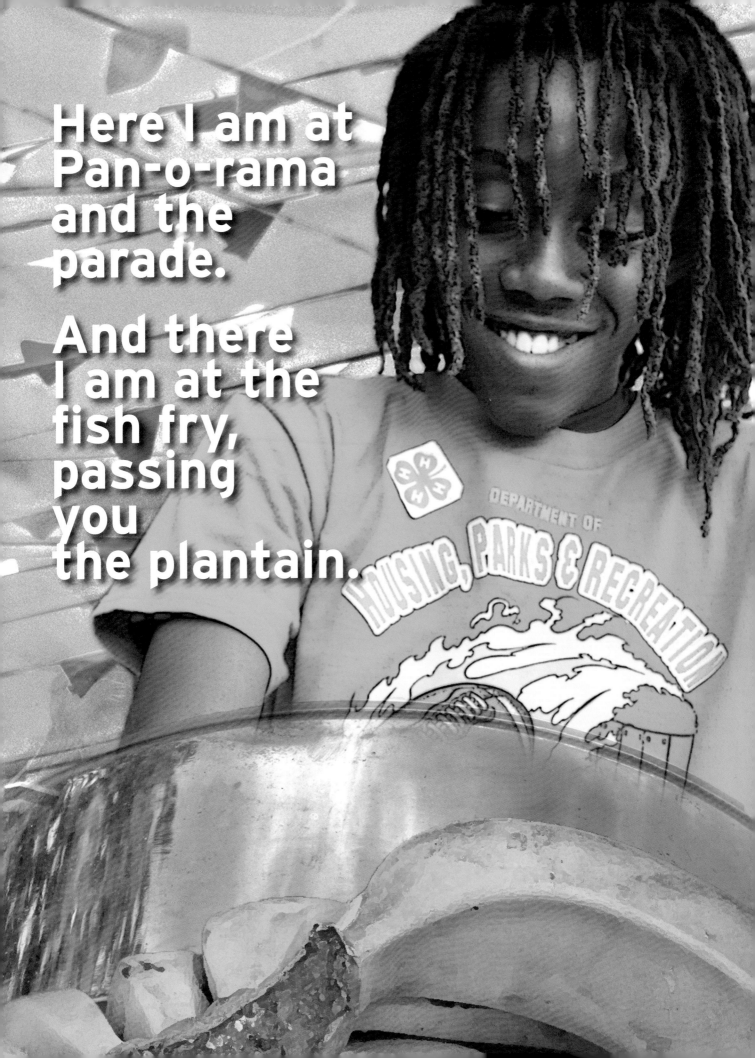

Here I am at Pan-o-rama and the parade.

And there I am at the fish fry, passing you the plantain.

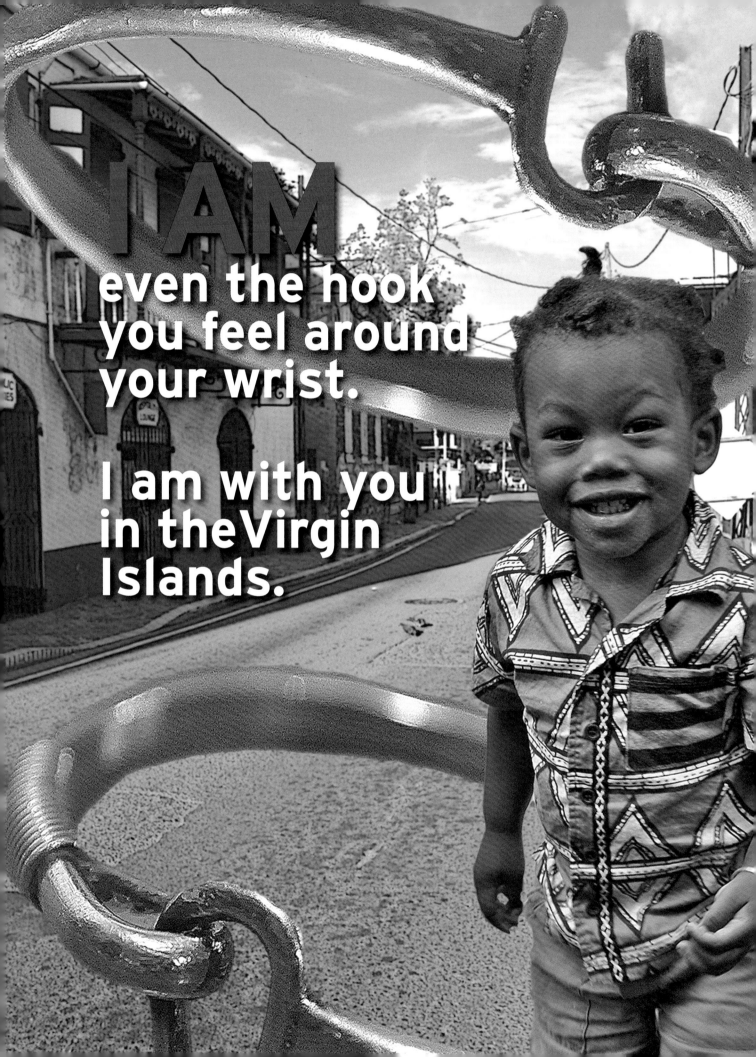

I AM even the hook you feel around your wrist.

I am with you in theVirgin Islands.

I am me
for **love**
of you—
the Virgin
Islands.

I AM the very soil and sand. I AM the coral beneath the water and the volcano beneath the land.

I AM senator and schoolteacher. I AM my grandmother and I am a quelbe band.

I AM. I AM.
I am all the I ams.

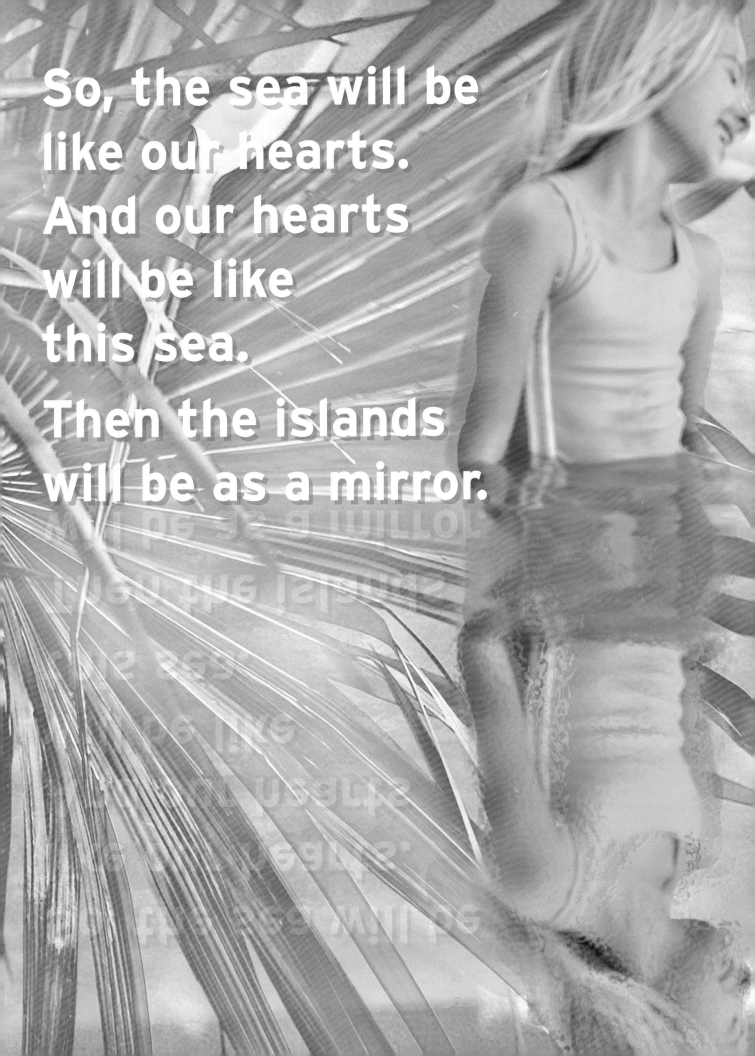

So, the sea will be
like our hearts.
And our hearts
will be like
this sea.

Then the islands
will be as a mirror.

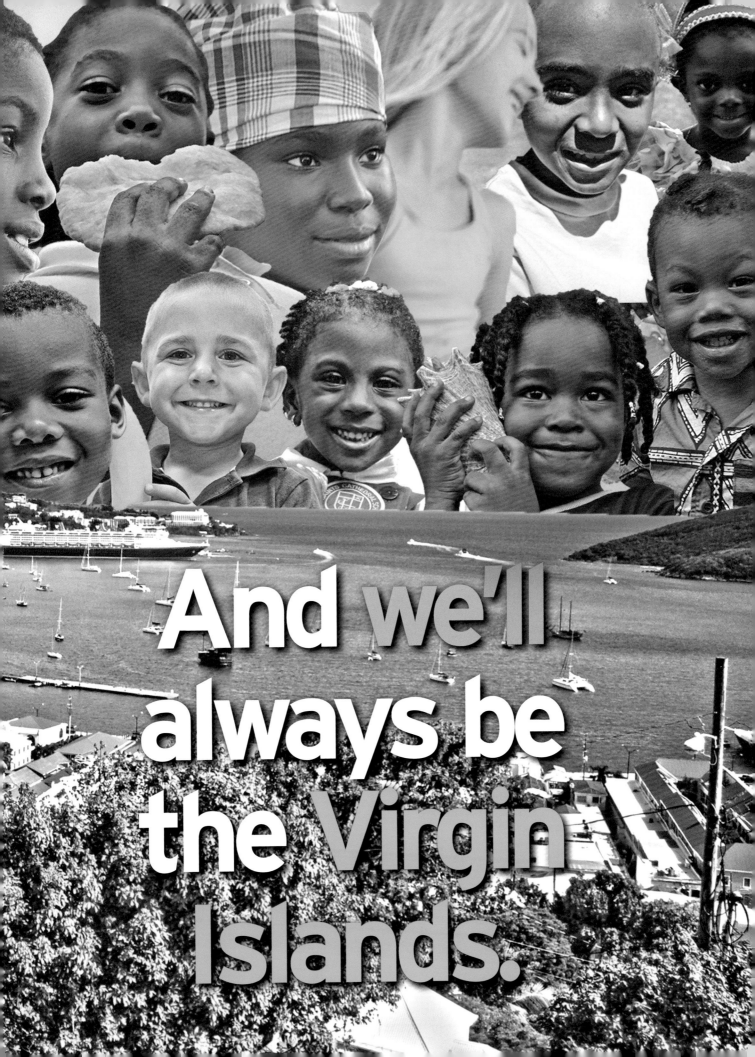

And we'll always be the Virgin Islands.

GLOSSARY

Coki Point Beach is located in the Smith Bay area of St. Thomas. It is a great beach for snorkeling and scuba diving.

Cruz Bay is one of the two towns on the island of St. John.

A **scratch band** is a band whose musicians often play handmade instruments. Some of the instruments are made up of a stick that scratches a base to make a melody. **Scratch band**s play **Quelbe** music.

A **steel pan** is an instrument originally made from oil barrels. Notes are pounded out and when played make a crisp ringing sound. The **steel pan** was invented on the island of Trinidad but is played all over the Caribbean, including the Virgin Islands.

Carnival is a time of cultural revelry in the Virgin Islands and throughout the Caribbean. Virgin Islanders wear costumes and dance in the streets. During Carnival many cultural elements not experienced throughout the year are featured. Many of the things mentioned in this book are often seen or experienced during Carnival.

Frenchtown is a village in the downtown area of St. Thomas. It is called Frenchtown because historically the people who live there are of French descent.

Frederiksted is one of the two cities on the island of St. Croix. Frederiksted is often called Freedom City, because it was where many important movements for Virgin Islands freedom were launched.

The ***Virgin Islands March*** is the national song celebrating the Virgin Islands. In the march, the islands are described as being **emeralds** of the sea.

Queen Mary was a community leader in **Frederiksted** who led a labor rebellion called the Fireburn. She fought for workers to be paid fair wages.

Coziah (also known as **Queen Coziah**) was a community leader in Charlotte Amalie, St. Thomas. She was a coal carrier. She led a protest for coal carriers to be paid fair wages.

The Night of the **Silent Drum** is the name of a slave revolt that took place in 1733 on the island of St. John. During this rebellion people who were not paid at all for the work they did decided to fight for their human rights.

Buddoe is the nickname for General Moses Gottlieb. General Gottlieb fought for enslaved Africans to be freed from slavery. On the day slavery was made illegal in the Virgin Islands **Buddoe** blew a conch shell to let everyone know that freedom had come.

Cyril King was the second elected governor of the Virgin Islands. He was very popular for many reasons; one being that he was comfortable interacting with Virgin Islanders of all kinds.

Petroglyphs are drawings carved into stone. In the Reef Bay area of St. John, there are petroglyphs surrounding a pool of water. Many scientists think that these drawings were made both by the Virgin Islands' original people, the Caribs and Arawaks, and by Africans who were brought to islands and then contributed their culture.

Hospital Ground is the official name for the Round da Field neighborhood in downtown St. Thomas. It is called **Hospital Ground** because it is where the island's hospital was first built. It is also sometimes called Round da Field because it was where the first ball field on the island was built. Tiphanie Yanique, the author of this book, is from **Hospital Ground.**

Madras cloth is a fabric with a colorful plaid design. It is called madras because it is originally from the Madras region of India. The Virgin Islands national dress is made of madras cloth.

Jawbone is a kind of mint candy. It is hard and shaped like a stick.

Johnny cake is a fried bread often eaten with cheese or fish for breakfast. It is also a side dish during lunch or dinner.

Pan-o-rama is a musical event held during **Carnival**. At **Pan-o-rama** all the **steel pan** bands on island come together to perform and compete.

A **fish fry** is an event where fried fish is the main dish. A **fish fry** is usually held in an open public place, like the beach or a parking lot.

Plantain is a fruit that is very similar to a banana. In the Virgin Islands **plantain** is eaten fried or boiled.

The St. Croix **hook** bracelet resembles the nautical knot used to dock boats. Legend goes that hook rings or bracelets were once used in the Virgin Islands as wedding bands.

Quelbe is what the national music of the Virgin Islands is often called. **Quelbe** music is usually played by a **scratch band**. Besides the homemade instruments, **Quelbe** is also characterized by word play and innuendo. The songs often describe things that have really happened in the Virgin Islands.

Notes for young poets, teachers and parents

Some of the poetic devices used in this book:

Alliteration
Metaphor
Repetition
Rhyme
Simile

Can you find where the poet uses these poetic devices?

Can you think of any other creative ways the poet uses language in this book?

YOU CAN WRITE AN *I AM* POEM

What is an *I am* poem?

An *I am* poem is a poetic form where you write about who you are in connection to something important to you. In this book it is about who the poet is in connection to the U.S. Virgin Islands. Your *I am* poem can be about your connection to whatever is important to you. Your family, your toys, your favorite book, your bedroom, your family, your favorite movie—anything you want.

One way to write an *I am* poem

- Make a list of the things you love in that place (these will be nouns).

- Make a list of what you like to do in that place (these will be verbs).

- Make a list of what the place looks, feels and smells like (these will be adjectives).

- Look at your lists again. Pick your favorite words from the lists that you made. Put the phrase "I am" in front of your favorite words. You can put them in order: nouns, then verbs and finally adjectives. You can mix them up. Or you can make complete sentences that include nouns, verbs and adjectives. With guidance second and third grade poets who write in complete sentences can be encouraged to write

metaphors. Instead of "I am playing video games in my room," you might write "I am the buttons and I am the controls. I am the win at the end."

- You can also put another phrase at the beginning. Instead of "I am" you can put "I dream about." You can even make up your own opening phrase.

- Don't be afraid if the poem feels strange. Some of the best poems in the world are strange.

Teachers and parents can help very young poets write a community poem with adult help. For example, a classroom *I am* poem where each student contributes a line based on their favorite thing about school or their classroom. Another example is a bedtime *I am* poem where each night a new line is added that mentions something fun the young poet did that day.

Though this book is focused on K-3 aged children, *I am* poems are written by poets at all levels. Poets in middle school, high school and beyond can write versions of the *I am* poem. More practiced poets can also address things that are more complex, such as things you don't like, things in your life that have been difficult or things that you are afraid of. Such as "I am loud noises in the dark" or even "I am the sadness when my grandmother died." After all even difficult things are part of who we are. Some examples of well known *I am* poems written by published writers are:

"I Remember" by Joe Brainard

"The Delight Song" by N. Scott Momaday

"Momma Sayings" by Harryette Mullen

"Where I'm From" by Willie Perdomo

Notes for young artists, teachers and parents

Can you guess what all the images are in one collage?

Can you guess what island is represented in each part of a collage?

Why do you think the artist created a particular collage to pair with the words in the book?

YOU CAN MAKE AN *I AM* COLLAGE!

A collage is a piece of art made up of different images, sometimes even different materials. Anything that you can fasten together on a background is a collage.

One way to make an *I am* collage

This is just one way to make a collage.

Collect scraps from around your house or from your community. Make sure these are things your family doesn't mind you using! You can collect postcards, leaves, shells, fabric from clothes that no longer fit you…anything. Take pictures of things in your room, home or community. For example: You can take pictures of your family members and toys. You can take pictures of your favorite foods and your friends. You can take pictures of yourself; your hands, your feet. You can even draw things.

You can cut out images or even rip them up. Cutting can be very neat, but ripping can be more fun and might even help you come up with strange and interesting designs.

To make your *I am* collage like the ones in this book make sure to put an image of yourself in the collage. You can also use an image that represents you. For example, you might use an image of your mother or an image of your favorite toy.

Pick a heavy piece of material for the background. Construction paper will work if your collage is mostly paper or other light materials. You may have to use a more sturdy background if you are using heavier materials.

Now laydown all your materials onto the background so you can decide where you want everything to go. You might order things together based on location or based on color or based on anything you want. It is okay if things overlap. Don't worry if your collage is messy. The best collages are sometimes messy and wild. Once you've decided how things will be laid out, you can begin to glue them down. Make sure to let your collage dry before hanging!

Teachers and parents can help students by giving them magazines, newspapers or over-used old books. To encourage creativity, give each student a few different kinds of sources: for example, a newspaper that is focused on where the student's are from, a magazine that is focused on a distant place, and a book geared towards the student's age group. Students can use the first half of class to cut out images that they like and images that they feel most represent them. For older students another option is to give them one magazine that they may rip out under the pressure of a clock. After one minute they will have to switch. This will encourage intense observation. It might also be a lot of fun.

The collages in this book were made with photographs and "glued together" using digital software. Older artists can also use digital photographs to create collages on the computer using uploaded photography or scanned images.

Though this book is focused on K-3 aged children, collages are made by artists at all levels. Some well-known collagists are:

Romare Bearden

Bryan Collier

Hannah Höch

Pablo Picasso

"I am" Across the Curriculum

This book is one of art and literature but is also meant to be used for lovers and students of history and the social sciences. The various historical references in both the poem and the art can be used as prompts for students to learn about that particular history. Students in history class can also create *I am* poems based on historical figures. The *I am* poem can even be used to deepen learning and fun in the natural sciences and mathematics. It can help students learn the function and traits of a triangle, for example.

You can write an *"I am"* poem:

Thank you *to Robin Reagler and the Houston Writers in the Schools—*
"Tried and True: A Collection of Lessons from Writers in the Schools"
was a valuable resource, Amy Swauger and the Teachers & Writers
Collaborative, Summer "The Where I'm From Project: Connecting to
History and Community Through Poetry" published in the Teachers
and Writers Magazine gave us guidance, Willie Perdomo's "Where I'm
From" was an inspiration as was the collage by Romare Bearden. Special
thanks to Mario Picayo, Cecile de Jongh, Dave Schjang, Kalil Andrews,
Malik Andrews, CK Dodd, Na'jee Richardson, Nickolas Swan, Kelsey Swan,
Alvisha Rhymer, Elijah Bell, Keyanna Hazel, Kaelin Hodge, Devonte James,
Ja'Kalah Meade, Logan Dietsch, Kahare Donadelle, Keiron Charles, Trinity
Riggle, Isabella Hahnfeld, Jade Flood, Bilal D.K. Muhammad, Mikaili
Estrada-Petersen, Deena Smith, Krishiv Amarnani, Dave Schjang, Elisabeth
Anderson, the students of All Saints Cathedral School, Principal Yvonne
Barry and Ms. Foster, Rising Stars Youth Steel Orchestra and more broadly
to all the people of the Virgin Islands who simply by being beautiful and
keeping the Virgin Islands a beautiful place to be were an inspiration for
this book. Finally, thank you to the late Beaulah Smith Harrigan, for the
camera.

About the author

Tiphanie Yanique is a writer and teacher from the Virgin Islands. She is a professor of creative writing at The New School. Her collection of stories set in the Caribbean and around world is called *How to Escape from a Leper Colony.*

Moses Djeli is a photographer and teacher from Florida. He loves the Virgin Islands. He teaches with the New York City Department of Education. To see more of his photography visit mosesdjeli.tumblr.com.

About the artist

Moses and Tiphanie live with their son between Brooklyn and the Virgin Islands.

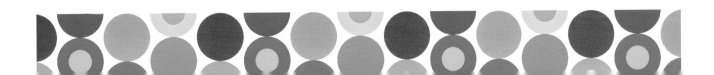

Published by Little Bell Caribbean, an imprint of Editorial Campana

For information, address, permissions:
Little Bell Caribbean
An imprint of Editorial Campana
19 W 85th St.
New York, NY 10024
www.campanitabooks.com

Book design by Yolanda V. Fundora / www.urban-amish.com
Editor-in-Chief: Mario Picayo
Production: McKinley Matteson

Library of Congress Cataloging-in-Publication Data

Yanique, Tiphanie.
  I am the Virgin Islands / by Tiphanie Yanique and Moses Djeli. -- 1st ed.
     p. cm.
   ISBN 978-1-934370-30-8 (hardcover)
  1. Virgin Islands of the United States--Juvenile poetry. I. Djeli, Moses. II. Title.
   PS3625.A679I25 2012
   811'.6--dc23
                            2012026153

Manufactured in the United States of America

First edition, January 2013

    9 8 7 6 5 4 3 2 1